Starting Slowly...

How many dates with a new person do you require before you:

Are willing to have sex?

Are willing to perform or receive oral sex?

Are willing to sleep the entire night in your new lover's bed?

Not a Matter of *If*...

For the ladies, on a scale of 1-10, how important is the size of a man's penis?
(1 = not at all important, 10 = a potential deal-breaker)
For the guys, using the same scale, how important are a women's looks in terms of wanting to sleep with her?

No Fractions Allowed

How many times per week do you *need* it?

And how many times per week do you *want* it?

Blacklisted

Which of the following would you *never* do?
One-night stand
Group sex
Swinging
Public sex (exhibitionism)
Three-way
Cuckolding (Google it ☺)

Tantric

In terms of duration, how long is too long?

And how long is just right?

Guessing Game

If you're in a group of five or more people, each person must call out the *number* of other people in the room they'd consider sleeping with. (Don't say their names…unless you want to.)

If the group is smaller, each person calls out the *number* of people at their place of work they'd consider sleeping with.
(Again, don't say names unless you want to.)

That Thing With Her Mouth

Name one thing that if your lover does during sex or foreplay that you're powerless to resist.
In other words, after they do it, you become *theirs*.

Tit for Tat

If you have sex with someone and *they* orgasm, but *you* don't, are you upset afterward?
If so, do you keep subtly quiet about it?
Or do you let them know?

Toys

Of the following items, name which ones are fair game for you or your partner to use during a sexual encounter:

A soft whip
Handcuffs
A dildo
A blindfold
Anal beads
Whipped cream

Get...Out

In terms of earning a second date with you, which of the following are deal-breakers?

Bad kissing
Your date was too aggressive
Your date wasn't assertive enough
You had a mild argument during the first date
You had an awful dinner at a place you didn't like
You had awkward sex on the first date

Sex in the Shadows

Choose which level of lighting you prefer during sex:

Total darkness
Dim, romantic candlelight
A lamp in the background and a window open to let moonlight in
Lights on, baby!

Hard to Compete with North and Grey

Estimate the total number of hours you've spent in your entire life watching porn.

Estimate the number of orgasms you've had while watching it.

If you said zero to either of these, break out the polygraph machine.

The Tease

Suppose that for the next week, for *non-serious* medical reasons, you couldn't have sex with your new partner.
The problem is; you're *dying* to get it on with them. After all, you're newly together, and everything is exciting with them.
Since you want them to be ready for action the *instant* the week ends, would you tease them? If so, how?
If not, would you stay away from them so as not to torment them?

Rare or Medium-Well

Choose your favorite style:

A. Making Love
B. Quickies
C. Fucking Hard
D. Marathon Sex
E. Just Get it Over With

White Flags

Give a number for each of these:
Approximately how many times (consecutively) would your partner have to
turn down sex with you before you:
Started a conversation about it?
Stopped initiating sex with them?
Considered having an affair?

Sex Scholarship

Suppose you've been dating someone new.
They're attractive, smart, and funny.
But so inexperienced sexually they're borderline bad at it.
Would you stay with them and use your experience to teach them how to be a
better lay?
Or move on to someone else?

All About That *Unnnhhh…*

What style or genre of music is best to have sex with?

Name two songs you wouldn't mind getting down and dirty with.

A Quick Drinking Game

Which of the following would you be willing to do?
For each one you say *NO* to, take a drink.
Play naked Twister
Watch a live sex show
Watch your partner get a strip dance
Attend a naked foam party (Google it if you need to ☺)
Have sex while other people watched

Evaporation

It's scientifically known that, *by and large*, human sexual attraction is driven by biology. Meaning that even if you love someone to death, it's possible (even probable) that at some point during your lives, you'll lose your sexual attraction to them.

If this were to happen to you or your partner for an extended time, how do you think you'd cope?

Cream of the Cream

Describe the best single night (or day) of sex you've ever had.

If your current partner is in the room, it's strongly recommended you limit yourself to encounters involving *them*. ☺

Read the Rest Tomorrow

If, instead of reading this book, you could be having sex *right now…*
…would you?
With whom?

Two Ships in the Night

Which of the following would prevent you from dating someone you're
otherwise attracted to?
Different religion
Different race
An age gap of 10 years
An annual income gap of more than $30,000
A 90 minute drive to reach their house

Explicitly Speaking

Imagine it's an average day.
You're sitting in bed alone.
A sexual thought pops into your head.
On a scale of 1-10, with 1 being not at all graphic or arousing, and 10 being extremely graphic and realistic, how explicit is *your* typical sexual fantasy?

It's Like Pizza

A somewhat popular view of sex (usually from the male perspective) is that *even when it's bad, it's good.*
With that in mind, is having bad or below average sex better than having no sex at all?

Eons

How much time do you require between sexual encounters *with different partners* in order not to feel icky?

(Fun Fact: During research, the average answer was a much shorter amount of time than expected.)

6.5 Deadly Sins

Is it acceptable to lust after someone else's spouse as long as the person doing the lusting never acts on it?
What if the object of the lust isn't married, but simply has a boyfriend/girlfriend?
What if the object of the lust whispers that the feeling is mutual (but still doesn't reciprocate)?

Brave Love Slave

For each of the following, admit to the ones you've fantasized about:
Cross-Dressing
Rape Fantasy
Sleeping With a Same-Sex Partner
BDSM
Being Part of a Gang Bang

Whoever admits the most gets free drinks for the rest of the night...

Slutty

Don't be confused by the word '*slutty.*'
This question is for both girls *and* guys.
How many different people could you f**k in one year before you'd start feeling too promiscuous?

Lava or Ice

Let's play a game. For each one of the following scenarios, call out HOT or
COLD, meaning the effect it'd have on your libido:
Sex with an ex
Role-playing your lover's teacher/schoolgirl fantasy
Sex with a stranger wearing a mask at a Halloween party
Phone sex with someone you've never met face-to-face before
Being a voyeur at a swinger's club
Having sex with a stranger, while their <u>spouse</u> is watching

Minimum Wage

Name the amount of time, in terms of *days/weeks/months* you could go
without sex before you began to feel depressed or anxious.

Or could you go forever without it and suffer no serious side-effects?

Street Cred

Of the following terms, name the ones you're familiar with:
Hotwife
Hentai
Creampie
Facial
Bukkake
Xenophiliobia (Extra credit if you know this one)

Sex Objects

Is it ever ok to sexually objectify someone you're dating or married to?
As in treat them like a sex object?
If so, just once in a while?
Only during sexual encounters?
Or is it acceptable to do more often, so long as it's not *all* the time?

Hanging From the Ceiling Fan

Name your top two sexual positions.

Explain why they're your favorites.

Sexilosophy

Is sex purely physical?
*As in; while it might make the participants feel great for a while, is it
ultimately just two people smashing their private parts together?*
Or is sex (at least sometimes) a deeper experience?
*As in; can it connect two people on a spiritual level and possibly even
enlighten them?*

The Squishiest Profession

Suppose you're flat broke.

You've run out of money and food. You won't be able to get a real job in the foreseeable future.

To survive, which of the following things would you rather do than sell your sexual services for cash?

Sell Drugs   Steal   Blackmail Someone
Volunteer for Medical Testing   Panhandle
Ask a Friend for a Huge Loan   Move in with Mom

Can You Last 10?

This game requires two partners to be alone together.

Unless you're kinky and want to be watched.

<u>This is how you play:</u>

One person finds somewhere comfy to sit or lie down naked.

And continues to read this book and answer questions.

The other person does everything in their power to make the reader orgasm.

If the pleasure-giver makes the reader an orgasm before 10 questions, they win, and the reader has to return the favor.

Pick-a-Part

Imagine someone you're highly physically attracted to.
Name them aloud.
Now describe what body part of theirs you most desire to touch, and what
you'd like to do to it.

Baseball

Guys: While a woman is working you over in bed, do you ever purposely
think about non-sexual things in order to avoid orgasming?
Girls: If you knew a guy was doing this, would you ever be annoyed or
offended?

Dear Horny:

If your current partner is in the room, give them one friendly tip for playing in the bedroom with you.

If not, offer up one piece of sex advice you'd like to give the whole world.

Lust Buster

Do you believe mind-blowing sex more often happens between two people who are *in love*?
Or can great sex happen consistently between people without any deeper connection?

50 Shades of _____

A famous author has just written an erotica novel based on your sex life.
Give it a title.

Make it Rain

Suppose you've just started dating someone new.
Neither of you are virgins.
Before you get intimate for the first time, how many showers would you like
your new prospect to have taken since last having sex with their previous
mate?
Try to give an exact number.

Porntanamo Bay

Speaking for yourself, name the worst (*or best*) possible sexual torment. In other words, what would drive you so crazy that you're not sure you could (*or would want to*) handle it?

Smolder

Which of the following do you prefer to do before getting down and dirty? Name as many as you like.

Have a drink
Shower immediately before
Enjoy extended foreplay
Have a sexy conversation
Tease
Be teased
Cuddle

Ambush

Suppose you're planning a Sex Trap for your partner.
When they get home, you'll have it all waiting: the lure, the setting, the diabolical plan to fall upon your unsuspecting prey and make them yours.
Well?
Describe your perfect trap.

Just Shut Up and F Me

Which of the following words might annoy or offend you if uttered by your partner during sex?
And which of the following words would you probably never say?

Pussy   *Whore*   *Cock*
Rape   *Bitch*   *Cum*
Fuck   *Deeper*

Ruined for Everyone Else

Choose the form of your next lay:

1. Your partner wears you out utterly. Your sex is borderline violent. Afterward, you're a limp noodle, having orgasmed into complete oblivion.
2. Your partner washes over you like soft rain, treating you tenderly. After their worship of your body, you fall into gentle sleep like a feather.

Trading Places

If, for one day, you could be your partner *and* they could be you, would you make the swap?
If so, what would you do to them?
And just as importantly, what would you do to *yourself*?

Please?

This question is best answered in the presence of a lover.
…or a group of sarcastic yet understanding friends who will mock, yet sympathize with you.
Name the one thing, more than anything else, you wish your partner would try with you in bed.

I can't get *no...*

Describe what it takes to *completely* satisfy you in bed.
If it's even possible...
Be very specific.

The Sexeporter

A pink button rests before you.
If you push it, any one person (celebrity, historical figure, past flame, current crush, etc.) will be teleported to your bedroom for a full night of *whatever you want.*
Afterward, you'll never see them again.
Would you push the button?
If so, whom would you summon?

All Hallows

If you could choose, what sexy costume would you want your partner to wear on Halloween?
...even if just for the pure pleasure of tearing if off them later.

Swapping *Stuff*

Girls, if you could make your orgasms more like a guy's, as in being able to easily have one huge cum before being utterly satisfied, would you?
Guys, if you could cum more like a girl, as in being overcome by waves of epic, but more difficult to come by, orgasms, would you?

The Cum Dungeon

You're going to be stuck in a dungeon for the next three days.
The only way you'll get released is if you orgasm twenty times during a 72-hour span.
The good news: You get a few choices.
Who's stuck in the dungeon with you? (Can be 1 person or many)
What one toy do you have?
Pick one of the following: Towels, a bathtub, or lube

Under the Knife

In terms of trying to improve your *already strikingly good* looks,
if you could have swift, painless cosmetic surgery to alter any one part of
your body, which body part would you choose and what change would you
have made?
For purposes of this question, real science and medicine do not apply (i.e.;
you can get any cosmetic upgrade you can dream of.)

Worth Getting Fired For

Suppose you worked at an office in which dating your coworkers is strictly
forbidden.
Your salary at this office is $100k annually.
The one trouble: The person who sits two desks away is amazing, attractive,
and *completely* into you. You *need* to be with them.
(If it helps, pretend your current partner is this coworker.)
How would you break the system in order to date them?
Or would you take a lesser paying job?

Lonely Housewife seduces the Pool Boy

Here's your chance to role-play.
If you could choose, what's one scenario you'd like to role-play with your partner?
(Examples: *teacher/student, housewife/pool boy, guard/prisoner.*)
Don't just pick the roles.
Describe how the whole scenario would go down.

Skills for Thrills

Rank the following in order, highest to lowest, in terms of how much they'd influence you when deciding to date a new partner:
Your new partner is an amazing cook
They're a lights-out good dancer
They're laid back and easy to get along with
They're interested in many of the same things you are
They're mind-bogglingly good in bed

Breaking *You*

Falling in love tends to be an unpredictable event.
People never know when it could happen, nor where, nor how.
With that said, can you name three things that must happen in order for you to let love in?
In other words, what three things do you *have* to have in a potential partner for love to have any shot?

Genie in a Bottle

If you could name one thing, *just one*, that you wish your partner would try with you between the sheets, what would it be?
If they're in the room with you now, they must answer *Yes* or *No* as to whether or not they're willing to try this one thing.
If they say *No*, you get to keep wishing until they say *Yes*.
If your lover isn't here, what do you think the odds are they'll agree to your first wish?

Guinnesex Book of World Records

What's the longest you've ever lasted during a sexual encounter before
climaxing?
And what's the shortest you've lasted?
Bonus: If you're alone with your partner (or at some kind of awesome sex
party) challenge them to break the shortest record right now.
...and the longest record tomorrow.

Fill in the Blanks

Girls: If a guy does _____ to you before sex, you'll do almost
anything he wants afterward.

Guys: If a girl does _____ to you before sex, you'll probably
climax within moments.

Try Something New (or not)

Let's play a game.
This game is best played by couples who are alone.
On a small scrap of paper, each person playing must secretly write their top two favorite sex positions in order (*1 & 2.*)
Each person then reveals what they wrote.
If both of you chose the same #1 favorite position, toss this book aside and have sex right now using the chosen position.
If not, write down your next two favorites in secret and repeat.
The catch: You can't write the same position more than once.

The Scalpel or the Hammer

Let's get a little dark.
Think of some of the *less-than-awesome* sex experiences and relationships you've had.
Now choose one of the following:

- Erase one specific sexual encounter from existence
- Erase one entire romantic relationship from existence

Explain your choice.

Behind the Scenes

Do any movies of you performing sex acts exist?
If so, describe the best part.
If not, would you ever make a sex movie?
And would you care if it got out on the internet?

Worth the Wait?

Suppose you've started dating a new person.
They're smart, funny, and very attractive.
But they're making you wait for sex.
How many dates would have to go by before you brought up the lack of
intimacy?
And how many more dates before you considered ending the relationship due
to no sex?

Post-F**k Survey

After a particularly good lay, you're thinking:

_____

or maybe even

_____

Timing is Everything

Which of the following sexual encounters sounds the most appealing?
Spontaneous sex on a day you thought it'd never happen
First-time sex with an attractive new partner after a great date
Making love to your spouse in a fancy five-star hotel
Finally seducing someone you've pursued for an entire year
Having a mind-blowing one-night stand with someone beautiful

The Freak Test

On separate pieces of paper, everyone in the room writes their own name and the names of everyone else.

In secret, everyone writes a number between 1-10 beside each name.

Each number next to each name represents the *level of freakiness* that person is believed to have.

A rating of 1 means they're not sexually adventurous at all. A 10 means they'll do almost anything at almost any time.

Afterward, everyone reveals their paper and confirms/denies what other people ranked them.

Floodgates

Imagine scientists have invented a new kind of sex pill.

If you take this pill, you and any partner you sleep with will be *100% immune* to STD's and pregnancy.

Each dose lasts exactly one year.

If this pill were available, would you take it?

If so, imagine you're single. How would taking the sex pill influence your sex life?

Or is this pill of no interest to you?

The F-Bot 9000

Imagine you're single and in need of some action.
A tech company has just invented an *absolutely lifelike* robot for use as a sex partner/servant.
You can customize this robot however you like. It will do *whatever* you ask...*whenever* you ask it.
Would you invest in a F-Bot?
If so, how many years do you think you'd keep it around?

Aftermath

After having good sex (or any sex, for that matter) name which of these appeals to you the most:
Pillow talk
Cuddling
Sleep
A specific activity, such as _____
Take a quick breather, then have sex again

Tragic

Pretend that tomorrow will be the last day you'll get to spend with the love of your life for the next five years.
It's possible you'll get to be with them after the five years are up, but not guaranteed.
How would you spend your last day with them?
What would be the focus of your time together?
Would you bother with sex?

Just for the Girls

For each of the following, state whether or not you could be satisfied if your man made love to you for exactly that amount of time:

3 minutes
5 minutes
10 minutes
30 minutes
1 hour
1 ½ hours

Truth or Dare

You're in a hot tub with five other attractive people.
Your partner is there, as well as two other couples.
It's late. Everyone's had a few drinks.
Someone suggests playing Truth or Dare.
You all play, and the game starts to get sexual.
Everyone else in the hot tub is really, really enjoying it.
Name the dare that would make you stop playing.

And Now for the Guys

Do you always, *as in every single time*, want the woman you're sleeping with
to get max pleasure?
Is it ever all about you?
During any encounter in which it's all about you, is it because you sometimes
just need to get yours?
And is your partner usually ok with it…or not?

XXXBox 360

Suppose a video game company created a hyper-realistic sex simulator.
To play, all you have to do is slip on a pair of 4D goggles, select from a nearly limitless array of video game sex partners, and you'll be able to experience whatever kind of encounter you want…*whenever you want it.*
This 4D sex will feel real in every way, and will give you as many orgasms as you can handle.
How many times would you play per year?

Fetishes

The definition of a sexual fetish: *sexual desire in which gratification is linked to a particular object, item of clothing, part of the body, or specific behavior*
So…got a fetish?
If so, what is it?
If you met someone you really liked but who didn't share your fetish, would you stay with them?

The Pledge, the Turn, the Prestige

Suppose you're at a masquerade party.

Your costume is killer.

Turns out someone you *really, really* want to date is at the same party. They're an acquaintance, but not exactly a friend (yet.)

Trouble is; they look fantastic in their costume. Because of it, they're earning a lot of attention from *other* potential suitors.

If you don't act now, you might not see this person for several weeks.

Do you make your move tonight? If so, what's your strategy?

If not, why?

Girls' Sexy Shopping Cart

Ladies, it's time for a little fun. You have exactly $10 to go shopping for a new guy. *Go crazy.*

$3 – He's seriously hung $5 – He's 'David Beckham' handsome

$5 – He makes $1,000,000 annually $2 – He has great style

$3 – He's got a fantastic body $3 – No kids. No ex-wife. No baggage

$2 – He gives the world's best oral $1 – He's got awesome tattoos

$1 – He's a great kisser $1 – He's very affectionate

Guys' Horny Shopping Cart

Now it's the *guys'* turn. You have exactly $10 to go shopping for a new woman. *Go nuts.*

$5 – She's got a stunningly beautiful face $3 – She's in it for love, not money

$3 – She's got a swimsuit-model body $2 – She makes $1,000,000 annually

$2 – No kids. No ex-husband. No baggage $1 – She swallows

$5 – She loves sex exactly as much as you do $1 – She loves to cuddle

$1 – She likes to watch sports with you $3 – She has the world's best butt

Quickie Hits

For each of the following, pick your preference:
Be dominant or submissive?
Have sex first thing in the morning or right before bed?
Tipsy or sober?
Toys or no toys?
In the shower or in the bathtub?
With a lot of buildup or as a total surprise?

Sex Math

Solve the following equation:

_____ + _____

=

The best sex ever.

Start your Engine

How long does it usually take you to get mentally in the mood for sex?
And how long of touching, kissing, or playing does it take for you to get
physically ready?

*(Interesting Research Tidbit: Surprisingly, guys reported taking longer than
expected to get mentally in the mood.)*

Lasso the Moon

Which of the following would you be willing to do in order to get laid? (You can name more than one.) If you're currently in a relationship, assume *they* are the one you'll be sleeping with.

Skip two consecutive meals
Drive two hours (one way)
Take a sick day from work
Blow off a fun night out with friends
Skip an awesome event (concert, game, movie, etc.)

Resistance Should Be Futile

Imagine you're at home, but distracted by an important work project. You're sitting on the couch, laptop in your lap, typing away.
Think you could you resist sex it if your partner:
Kissed you softly on the neck?
Rubbed your thigh while you're typing?
Pushed your laptop away and made out with you?
Slithered up next to you while naked?

For fun, role-play this scenario and see how long you last.

A F**k in the Road

Suppose you're running late to an important event.
But you're also so horny you're ready to pop.
There's no time for sex.
Guys, would you rather your woman give you a handjob, a blowjob, tease
you to work you up for later, or do nothing and wait for a more convenient
time?
Ladies, if anything, which would you rather do?

Dream Night

You're about to go out with someone you really, really like.
Money is no object tonight.
Nor is distance.
Where is your perfect night taking place?
What are you doing there?
If there's no sex involved, is that ok?

Horny Holiday

Suppose the country you live in decided to create a new national holiday.
On this special day, no one is supposed to go to work or do any chores.
They're just supposed to make love all day long.
Think you'd fully participate? As in…make your country proud?
Or is it just another day to barbeque and not be at work?

Coitus Interruptus

You're having sex.
It's good. Maybe not great. But good.
Would any of the following make you stop?
Your phone goes off
Your baby cries
The doorbell rings
The timer on the oven beeps
You hear a car crash outside your window

10 Points of Foreplay

Let's play a game. For each of the following things, assign a point value 0-10 in terms of how close it'd get you to wanting sex. 0 points means it does nothing for you. 10 points means after it happens you're ready to go:

Kissing   Dancing   Drinking
Sexting   Holding Hands   Good Conversation
Eye Contact   Seeing Him/Her Naked
Cuddling   Just Being Alone Together

Lights, Camera, Orgasm

You and your favorite sex partner have been recruited to be the stars of an upcoming adult movie.
The movie will be one hour long.
If you manage to arouse audiences, you'll earn $1,000,000.
The catch: you and your partner are 100% in charge of deciding how to sex it up during the movie.
So...how does your sex script go?

But Seriously…

If you're in a committed relationship, do you have any obligation at all to
sleep with your partner on a regular basis?
Does your partner share the same obligation?
Other than health issues, can you name three legitimate excuses for *not*
having sex?

Drawing Lines

If a forty-year old told you they'd slept with 25 different partners during their
lifetime, would you consider them to be of *questionable morals*?
What about 50 different partners?
100?
500?
1,000?

The Bargain

This question is most fun if played with a sex partner.
Suppose that in order to stay in a relationship with your lover you had to sign an unfair contract:
The contract states: *For the next 365 days, you're not allowed to kiss, fuck, or touch your lover.*
However, the contract can be made null and void if you allow your lover to sleep with three different people of their choice, one time each.
Suffer *or* let them cheat? If they'd cheat, have them name the three people they'd have sex with to break the contract.

One Unforgettable Night

Imagine your mate has offered you a one-time deal:
Tomorrow night, you can have *three-way sex* with any other two people in the world.
Your mate can be one of the two, but they don't *have* to be.
Can you name the two people you'd bang?
Or will you respectfully decline the opportunity?

Neverland

In terms of sex, name at least two things you'd *never* be willing to try with your mate.

As in: if they suggested them, you might leave the room.

Would You Rather...

Pay for sex *or* get paid for sex?
Watch porn *or* read erotica?
Have sex at midnight *or* right before lunch?
Sleep with your boss to get promoted *or* don't and get fired?
Have amazing sex once per week *or* average sex every other night?
Go down on your partner *or* have them go down on you?

Falling

Are you capable of having sex without gaining any emotional attachment at all?
We're not talking about one-night stands.
We're talking about having a F-buddy who gives your body a workout on a regular basis.
Could you handle this arrangement without having feelings?
When *other* people say they can, are they lying to themselves?

Location is Everything

Guys, given the choice, what part of a woman would you most like to orgasm on...*or in*?

Women, similar question: where do you want your man to orgasm?

Mounting Everest

Consider all the sex partners you've ever had in your life.
Count all the one-night stands, the long-term relationships, the marriages, the fuck-buddies, etc.
If they had to be honest, how many of those people do you believe would say *you* were the best lay they ever had?
Give an exact number.

Made in the USA
Las Vegas, NV
20 December 2024

14933626R00031